A VISIT to the CHILDREN'S ZOO

By Barbara Shook Hazen

Pictures by
Mel Crawford

GOLDEN PRESS
Western Publishing Company, Inc.
Racine, Wisconsin

MANY ZOOS ARE DESIGNED ESPECIAL-
LY FOR CHILDREN. THE ONE IN THIS
BOOK IS BASED ON THE CHILDREN'S
ZOO IN CENTRAL PARK, NEW YORK.

SUSIE AND NED are visiting the Children's Zoo. It is a very special kind of zoo.

"Grownups can't even get in unless they go with one of us," says Ned proudly.

"Look," says Susie. "Most of the animals are little, too! Here's a baby kangaroo."

"I wonder if they have any guinea pigs like our pet, Mister Guinea Pig?" says Ned.

Here comes a woolly young llama.

"He has the longest eyelashes I've ever seen," says Susie.

The llama likes to have his back scratched. He would also like to eat the straw flowers on Susie's pocketbook.

But Susie says, "No, llama." She feeds him an animal cracker instead.

"Oh, it's nice and warm in here," says Ned. "This is where duck eggs are hatched."

The butter-yellow duckling babies are kept warm and snug until they are old enough to waddle out into the world.

Now it is time to visit the rabbits. The keeper brings them out. He puts them in the middle of a round drum.

Susie pats the snowy-white one. He is as soft as Susie and Ned's own pet, Mister Guinea Pig. And the pink inside his ears is pale as the pink inside a seashell.

Ned likes the black-and-white bunny with funny eye-patches best.

Ned feeds him a cracker—nibble nibble—until it is all gone.

Soon the keeper says, "Nap time!" and he takes the bunnies back to their cage.

The children walk down to the churning, turning Mill on the River Dee.

There they see
two floating swans,
five honking geese,
and a whole fleet of ducks with fancy feathers.

Ned holds out his hand. All the birds come bob-
bing by for bits of animal cracker.

Honk honk! Paddle paddle! Swish—Hmmmmm,
what a delicious crumb!

Something else lives in the water—a huge, blue, water-spouting whale!

His great red mouth is open wide. Both Susie and Ned can walk inside.

"Look!" says Susie. "He's swallowed a whole tankful of tropical fish."

"No wonder he spouts," says Ned. "Think how those fish must tickle his tummy!"

Part of the Children's Zoo is a farm. In the barnyard, Susie and Ned meet some old storybook friends.

They see the Three Little Pigs.

The first pig lives in a house made of straw. The second pig lives in a house made of sticks. And the third pig lives in a house made of bricks.

They see Baa Baa Black Sheep,

Brown Cow and

her spotted calf,

Little Gray Donkey,

and here a chick,

there a chick,

everywhere a chick!

"But there is nobody like Mister Guinea Pig," Susie says sadly.

Susie and Ned make some new friends at the farm.
Susie likes the young yak. What gentle eyes he has!
And such long, silky-soft hair!

Ned prefers the pair of shaggy Shetland ponies. He and Susie pat their velvety noses.

There are still so many things to see before it is time to meet Mother.

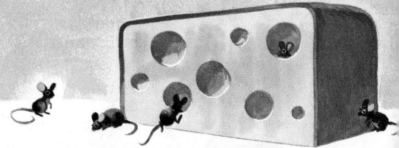

There's an apartment house for mice,

a monkey who dances to music,

tame deer who eat from your fingers,

and a talking bird with a bright orange beak.

And there are still so
many things to do.

Susie wants to listen
to story-telling time.

Ned wants to slide—woosh—
right down to the bottom
of the rabbit hole.

And both children want to feed
Bulldog Trash Basket.

And there are still places to visit.

Susie and Ned can't leave without seeing Hansel and Gretel's Candy Cane House, with its white-icing roof and gumdrop chimney.

"Let's go to the castle on the hill!" says Susie.

The castle has high turrets and towers. It is guarded by friendly goats with green-gold eyes.

From the tower window inside, Susie and Ned look down on the whole Children's Zoo.

They can see all the animals and all the things to do.

They can see the pond and the whale.

They can even see part of the park, the trees and the tall, tall buildings beyond.

As they are leaving the Zoo, Susie and Ned make
one last stop—Noah's Ark. Up the ramp they go, the
two of them, just the way Noah told the animals to go.

Inside the ark all the animals are ready for their long voyage.

And in one corner, can it be ... yes, it is! It is a snow-white guinea pig. He is fat and furry and friendly. He looks just like Susie and Ned's own pet, Mister Guinea Pig!

Ned runs to Mother, who is waiting by the gate. "Guess what!" he says. "We saw a guinea pig just like ours."

"He even squealed the same way," Susie says. "Oh, when can we come back and visit him?"

Mother smiles and says, "Very soon—that is, if you'll take me along with you. I'd like to meet that guinea pig—and all the other animals, too!"